THE AUTHOR

KU-595-910

Jim Slater was born on 29th October, 1903 at Gordon Cottage, Fountain Street, Banff. His parents, James Slater and Helen Mair, had unusual family connections in that five members of the Slater family married five of the same family of Mairs.

Jim's mother died in 1909 when he was only six years old, so during his father's lengthy absences at sea, he and two of his sisters were boarded out with a succession of relatives and friends. Eventually the children acquired a step-mother who hailed from Portsoy, and it was there that the family made their home after the death of Jim's father in 1916.

By that time Jim was fourteen and had just left Banff Academy (now Banff Primary School). He started work as a "half share loon" on a small boat working haddock lines from Portsoy and he recalls the three adult crew members as John Wood (Johnny Doo), George Harthill (Dod), and John Wood (Carrots). Jim continued as a fisherman till 1939 having meanwhile married a Portsoy lass, Helen Pirie. They were happily married for more than fifty years and Helen was of great assistance with her husband's research on the history of the area.

Jim joined the Merchant Service on the eve of World War 2 and served throughout the war as an engineer on the coasters. The next twenty-two years were spent as a driver in his step-brother's haulage business, but after he reached retiring age he worked for a few years at the local salmon fishing.

He tells us that the most momentous event of his life happened in March, 1923, when he was converted during a spiritual revival at Portsoy. The Scriptures have been the mainstay of his life ever since and his quiet, steadfast faith permeates his numerous writings in prose and in verse. His favourite topics are the history of Portsoy and the life, customs and religious influences of north-east fisher folk.

FOREWORD

"They that go down to the sea in ships, that do business in great waters; these see the works of the Lord, and His wonders in the deep."

The truth of these words is reflected in this interesting record of fishing boat names, chosen from the Bible, or linked with its principles and teaching.

This practice was more in evidence in the days of the sail-boat, when fishermen were very much exposed to the vagaries of wind, tides, and weather, than with the men of today who have shelter decks and technology that makes navigation easier, and sea-faring life more comfortable, than it was in grand-father's day.

The list covers a period of approximately one hundred years, and includes most types of fishing craft in general use around our shores; Scaffies, Fifies, Zulus, steam and motor drifters, seiners and trawlers.

It is recognised that some men, in naming their boats, may not have had Bible references in mind when they did so. For example, if someone chose the name Morning Star he may have been thinking of the dawn he had so often witnessed in his life at sea. Since it is well-nigh impossible for the author to differentiate in this, all names with an obvious Biblical connection have been included.

Fishing vessels often change owners, by sale or otherwise, so the name, as a result of this, can be carried over to another port of registry. Thus some of the boats may be mentioned more than once, with the same name but a different registration number.

No claim is made that this is a complete record, but it is hoped that what is here provided, will be of personal interest and educational value.

The next section demonstrates the theme which the Admiralty chose in naming the "Standard" drifters built during World War I, (1914-19) The term 'standard' was a word used by the fishermen to describe the fact that these boats were built to a recognised specification in size and power.

Part 2 reminds us of the generosity of Madame Simone Prunier, and her interest in the herring fishermen, in providing for them a Trophy with the accompanying awards.

I am grateful to the staff of Aberdeen City Libraries for providing the Reading List which forms Part 3, and I hope that my poems in Part 4 will give pleasure to all my readers.

J.S.

CONTENTS

A LIST OF BRITISH FISHING VESSELS
WITH BIBLICAL NAMES

Registration Letters

A	- Aberdeen	LA	- Llanelly
AA	- Alloa	LH	- Leith
AH	- Arbroath	LI	- Littlehampton
B	- Belfast	LK	- Lerwick
BA	- Ballantrae	LN	- Lynn
BCK	- Buckie	LO	- London
BF	- Banff	LT	- Lowestoft
BK	- Berwick	LY	- Londonderry
BM	- Brixham	M	- Milford
BN	- Boston	ME	- Montrose
BRD	- Broadford	ML	- Methil
BS	- Beaumaris	N	- Newry
BW	- Barrow	NN	- Newhaven
CA	- Cardigan	OB	- Oban
CH	- Chester	P	- Portsmouth
CK	- Colchester	PD	- Peterhead
CN	- Campbeltown	PH	- Plymouth
CS	- Cowes	PW	- Padstow
CY	- Castlebay	PZ	- Penzance
D	- Dublin	R	- Ramsgate
DE	- Dundee	RO	- Rothesay
DO	- Douglas	S	- Skibereen
E	- Exeter	SA	- Swansea
FD	- Fleetwood	SE	- Salcombe
FR	- Fraserburgh	SH	- Scarborough
FY	- Fowey	SM	- Shoreham
GN	- Granton	SN	- S. Shields
GU	- Guernsey	SR	- Stranraer
GY	- Grimsby	SS	- St. Ives
H	- Hull	SY	- Stornoway
HL	- Hartlepool	TH	- Teignmouth
IH	- Ipswich	TT	- Tarbert
INS	- Inverness	UL	- Ullapool
J	- Jersey	WK	- Wick
K	- Kirkwall	WY	- Whitby
KY	- Kirkcaldy	YH	- Yarmouth

A question mark following a name or port symbol indicates that the Port of Registry and/or the number are not known.

ABANA BF 790, BF 985	2 Kings 5:12
ABDIEL KY 95	1 Samuel 9:1
ABSTAINER BF 176, BF 302, BF 347, BF 1178, BF 1768, BF 2063	1 Thessalonians 5
ACACIA BF 199, BRD 133, DO 19, FR 390, PZ 319	Exodus 25:5
ACACIA WOOD INS 205	Exodus 25:5
ALPHA BF 58, BF 266, BF 354, BF 773, INS 259, SY 130, SY 409, WK 453	Revelation 1:11
AMETHYST AA 37, BA 81, BA 123, BCK 80, H 455, LK 635, PD 74	Revelation 21:20
ANCHOR OF HOPE DO 54, FR 214, ME 261, PD 358, PD 484, PD 894	Hebrews 6:19
AQUILA BCK 214, FR 105, LK 319, OB 99, PD 220	Acts 18:18
ARCTURUS BCK 103, BCK 242, BF 89, FD 6, LH 53	Job 9:9
ARIEL BCK 220, LH 446	Ezra 8:16
ARIMATHEA BF 782, LT 1084	Matthew 27:57

ARK B 891, LK 301	Genesis 6:14
ATHENIAN GY 357	Acts 17:21
AZARAEL FR 57	Nehemiah 12:36
AZAREEL KY 169, PD 76	Nehemiah 12:36
BALM BF 1174, BF 1871	Jeremiah 8:22
BDELLIUM FR 185	Genesis 2:12
BE FAITHFUL B 10	Revelation 2:10
BENAIAH N 208	2 Samuel 23:20
BERACHIAH B 322	Zechariah 1:1
BE READY BF 304, BF 337, FR 181, N 236, N 258	Matthew 24:44
BERYL BCK 46, BCK 131, BF 13, BF 106, BF 357	Revelation 21:20
BETHANY BF 1443	Matthew 21:17
BETHEL BF 793, BK 130, BK 201, BK 275	Genesis 28:19
BETTER HOPE BF 1047, GY 272, KY 212, LH 68, WK 138	Hebrews 7:19
BEULAH ML 66	Isaiah 62:4

BEZALEEL BF 262, K 27, PD 258	Exodus 31:2
BLASTUS BF 165	Acts 12:20
BRETHREN BF 1055	Romans 12:1
BRIGHTER HOPE BF 59, BF 65, CN 16, FR 371, HL 44, KY 327, LH 68, LK 241, LK 502, PD 113 PD 155, PW 119	Hebrews 7:19
BROTHERLY LOVE BF 433	Romans 12:10
BUCKLER LT 756	2 Samuel 22:31
CAPTIVE MAID BF 580	2 Kings 5:2
CARMI BCK 22, BF 256, INS 548, LH 204	Joshua 7:1
CARMI III KY 300	Joshua 7:1
CARPENTER'S SON BF 379, BF 471	Matthew 13:35
CEDAR BF 520, BF 733, BF 1576, BRD 258 INS 324, K 123	1 Kings 5:6
CEDRON BF 991	John 18:1
CENTURION BF 1278	Matthew 27:24
CHARISMA BF 296, FR 75, LK 352	Romans 5:16

CHARITY SY 399	1 Corinthians 13:1
CHILDREN'S FRIEND BF 27, BF 273, BF 1149, BK 177, FD 225, FY 255, KY 205, KY 346, LH 177, LT 537, PH 393, PZ 619, SN 329, SR 1, WK 149	Matthew 19:14
CHRISTIAN A 177, BF 570	Acts 26:28
CHRISTIANS BF 188	Acts 26:28
CHRYSOLITE BA 121, BA 301, BF 201, BF 274, BF 1662, CN 368, DO 71, FR 276, GY 260, INS 17, K 122, LH 190, LH 206, ML 237, SY 172	Revelation 21:20
COLOSSE BF 1054	Colossians 1:1
CONSTANT FAITH FR 303, INS 261, LT 1172, N 269, PD 83, PD 290, PD 334, SY 118	Colossians 2:5
CONSTANT FRIEND BM 222, FR 295, LT 1172, PD 83, PD 290	Proverbs 18:24
CONSTANT HOPE BF 284, KY 100, KY 383, LT 32	1 Peter 1:13
CORINTH INS 258	Acts 19:1
CORNELIUS ?	Acts 10:1
CRYSTAL RIVER B 346, BCK 16, BF 32, BF 129, FR 71, FR 278, LK 290, WK 113	Revelation 22:1

CRYSTAL SEA BA 104, BF 218, CN 314, FR 340, H 102, LH 97, N 243, OB 104, OB 145	Revelation 4:6
CRYSTAL TIDE BF 135	Revelation 4:6
CRYSTAL WATERS BF 209, SH 15	Revelation 4:6
DAMASCUS BF 133, INS 379	Genesis 14:15
DAN BF 1700	Genesis 30:6
DARDA BCK 99	1 Kings 4:31
DAY DAWN BF 189, BF 503, BF 524, BF 582, BF 1712, DE 168, FR 66, K 691, LH 187, LK 138, LK 691, ME 101, N 182, PD 136	2 Peter 1:19
DAYSPRING AH 165, BF 262, BF 312, BF 391, BF 456, BF 485, BF 500, BF 644, BF 1125, BF 1696, DE 51, FR 120, FR 198, FR 306, INS 122, K 877, LH 342, LH 487, PD 35, PD 219, PD 288	Luke 1:78
DAY STAR B 131, BF 221, BF 259, BF 532, BF 1112, FR 86, H 542, INS 317, WK 84	2 Peter 1:19
DELILAH BF 1258	Joshua 16:4
DELIVERER BF 67, BF 151	Romans 11:26
DIADEM BF 696, BF 1077, BF 1847, CA 145, CY 343, INS 154, LT 274, YH 377	Job 29:14

DIOSCURI BF 151, N 379	Acts 28:11
EASTER MORN B 95, BCK 2, BF 76, BW 218, DO 46, FD 215, INS 150, WY 61	Matthew 28:1
EBENEZER A 478, BCK 160, BCK 229, BF 23, BF 108, BF 338, BF 435, BF 637, BF 661, BF 923, BF 972, BF 1015, FR 133, FR 270, FR 282, INS 175, K 542, LH 136, LH 376, LK 192, ME 15, ML 33, ML 154, PD 45, SS 340, SY 51, WK 135, WK 278	1 Samuel 4:1
EL HANAN FR 152	2 Samuel 21:19
ELIEZER CN 9, LH 439	Genesis 15:2
EMERALD BA 283, BF 714, BF 792, BF 1080, FR 210, FR 289, GY 613, LK 674, N 388, YH 162	Exodus 28:18
EMMANUEL BK 91, GY 800	Matthew 1:23
EPHESIAN GY 63	Acts 19:28
EPHRAIM FR 3	Genesis 41:52
EPHRATAH A 659, BF 743, PD 5, PD 170	Psalms 132:6
ERASTUS PD 121	Acts 19:22
ESCHOL BF 291, FR 248, INS 154	Numbers 13:23

13

ESTHER BN 51, LT 505	Esther 2:7
EUPHRATES LH 80	Genesis 2:14
EUROCLYDON TH 77	Acts 27:14
EXODUS GU 117	Luke 9:31
FAIR HAVENS BF 134, KY 173, TT 140	Acts 27:8
FAIR WEATHER BF 319, PD 107, PD 132, PD 157, PD 307, PD 603	Matthew 16:2
FAITH KY 443, SH 21	Hebrews 11:1
FAITHFUL AH 97, B 100, BA 296, BCK 34, BF 205, BF 1703, BK 30, BK 39, BK 100, BK 101, BK 152, BK 204, BK 246, BS 129, CK 135, CK 154, FR 62, FR 129, FR 246, H 160, INS 38, INS 262, KY 80, ML 240, PD 11, PD 67, PD 307, PD 447	Revelation 2:10
FAITHFUL PROMISE B 260	Hebrews 11:11
FESTUS BF 1704	Acts 24:27
FIDELES N 219	Revelation 2:10
FIDELIS B 278, FR 319, FR 404, LH 125	Revelation 2:10

FORTUNATUS　　　　　　　　　1 Corinthians 16:17
BF 1315, BF 1750, CN 10, KY 144, LH 432,
YH 707

FRUITFUL　　　　　　　　　　　Colossians 1:10
A 99, B 79, BCK 194, BCK 333, KY 237,
PD 354, WK 59

FRUITFUL BOUGH　　　　　　　　Genesis 49:22
FR 196, INS 269, LK 403, PD 109, PD 477

FRUITFUL VINE　　　　　　　　　Psalms 128:3
FR 195, OB 309, PD 419

GALILEE　　　　　　　　　　　　John 2:1
BRD 105, WY 68

GALILEAN　　　　　　　　　　　Luke 22:59
FR 68, FR 136, GY 603, LT 1128, PZ 131

GLAD TIDINGS　　　　　　　　　Luke 1:9
AH 213, BF 73, BF 639, BF 872, BF 947,
BF 1152, BK 10, CN 202, INS 625,
LH 179, PD 182

GOLDEN BELLS　　　　　　　　　Exodus 28:33
AH 77, AH 162, BF 130, KY 192

GOLDEN HARP　　　　　　　　　Revelation 14:2
INS 404

GOLDEN RULE　　　　　　　　　Matthew 7:12
AH 33, AH 216, BCK 373, BF 238, BRD 856,
K 856, KY 335, SY 214, SY 225

GOLDEN SCEPTRE　　　　　　　　Esther 5:2
BF 152, BF 354

GOLDEN STRAND　　　　　　　　Revelation 21:21
B 83, BF 403, KY 107, OB 363, SY 41,
SY 173, SY 201

GOOD CHEER　　　　　　　　　　John 16:33
BK 1, BF 1940

GOOD HOPE　　　　　　　　　　　　2 Thessalonians 2:16
AH 18, AH 87, BCK 322, BCK 344, BF 41,
BF 145, BF 182, BF 203, BF 516, BF 622,
BK 87, CN 86, CY 30, FD 354, H 744, INS 487,
KY 365, LH 116, LN 139, PD 213, PD 356, PH 102,
TT 54, UL 10, UL 216, UL 336, WK 100, WK 209

GOOD NEWS　　　　　　　　　　　　Proverbs 25:25
BF 3, BF 2058, UL 79

GOOD SAMARITAN　　　　　　　　　Luke 10:33
ML 429, SY 355

GOOD SHEPHERD　　　　　　　　　John 10:14
BK 129, LA 4, LK 35, LK 716, LO 102

GOOD TIDINGS　　　　　　　　　　2 Kings 7:9
BF 1216, BF 1899, GY 4, LK 680, PD 182,
PD 246, PD 348

GRACE　　　　　　　　　　　　　　John 1:17
AH 460, BF 270, BF 1955, BK 32, ME 179

GREEN PASTURES　　　　　　　　　Psalms 23:2
AH 99, BCK 237, BF 7, FR 37, FR 72, FR 222,
KY 165, LH 424, N 20, N 210, PD 39

GUIDING STAR　　　　　　　　　　Matthew 2:9
A 777, AH 98, BCK 113, BF 29, BF 38,
BF 206, BF 304, BF 363, BF 444, BF 513,
BF 701, BF 732, BF 748, BF 1135, BF 1376,
BF 1790, BF 1899, FY 363, INS 247, K 531,
KY 322, LH 194, LH 382, LT 896, PD 132,
PD 322

HANNAH　　　　　　　　　　　　　1 Samuel 1:2
BF 1393

HARVEST GLEANER　　　　　　　　Ruth 2:3
BCK 120, BF 484, FR 73

HARVEST HOME　　　　　　　　　　Exodus 23:13
BF 425, LK 92, SA 92, TH 65

HAVILAH BF 161, N 12, N 200	Genesis 2:11
HAZAEL BCK 138, BCK 20, BF 1719, BRD 55, FR 107, FR 368, LO 2	1 Kings 19:5
HEBRON LH 294	Numbers 13:22
HEPHZI-BAH BF 2002, LH 153	2 Kings 21:11
HERITAGE BA 74, BF 150, BF 443, INS 247, LH 462, LT 509	Jeremiah 3:19
(OUR) HERITAGE FR 237	Jeremiah 3:19
HERMON BF 1293	Psalm 133:3
HOSANNA BF 1809, LT 167	Matthew 21:9
HYSSOP BF 1277, INS 77	Numbers 19:6
IMMANUEL BF 8, GY 602, WK 149	Isaiah 7:14
JACINTH BF 437, GY 383, LH 356	Revelation 21:20
JASPER AH 144, BF 3, BF 165, BF 611, BF 764, BF 1647, K 229, LK 144, PD 174, SY 379, SY 460	Exodus 28:17
JEREMIAH BF 705, BF 819, BF 1810	Jeremiah 1:1
JONATHAN BF 1210	1 Samuel 18:1

JOSEPH BF 927	Matthew 1:16
JUBILEE A 532, B 64, BF 201, BF 292, BF 319, BF 1355	Leviticus 25:8
JUDEAN GY 644	Acts 2:14
JUNIPER A 540	1 Kings 19:4
JUST REWARD KY 239, LT 592, LT 726	Hebrews 2:2
JUSTIFIED LT 240	Romans 3:6
JUSTIFIER LT 224	Romans 3:6
LABAN BF 313	Genesis 24:29
LAHAI-ROI LH 18	Genesis 24:62
LAUNCH OUT BF 250, BF 480, FR 37, KY 374, LK 428, LT 344, ML 455, PD 213, WK 347	Luke 5:4
LEBANON BCK 437, BF 1531, BF 1715, PD 509	Deuteronomy 1:7
LILY OF THE VALLEY BF 1300, BF 1422, CS 80, CY 194, LT 988, ME 63, ML 155, SY 996	Song of Solomon 2:1
LIVELY HOPE BA 98, BF 2, BF 1339, BK 91, LH 32, ML 198, PD 77	1 Peter 1:3
LYDDA BF 480	Acts 9:32

MAGDALEN KY 217	Matthew 27:56
MAID OF JUDAH BF 936, BF 1017	Lamentations 5:11
MAMRE OAKS BF 57	Genesis 23:17
MANNA BCK 3	Exodus 16:15
MANY WATERS BK 281	Psalms 29:3
MARANATHA FR 291, FR 375, UL 88	1 Corinthians 16:22
MARY BA 1, BF 66	Matthew 1:16

MIZPAH Joshua 11:3
A 26, A 451, BA 11, BA 12, BA 181,
BF 57, BF 79, BF 114, BF 178, BF 367,
BF 494 , BF 1165, BF 1639, BK 6, BK 72,
FR 223, GY 518, INS 99, INS 118, INS 564,
KY 18, KY 199, LH 181, LK 64, LK 209,
LN 84, ME 14, NN 120, SM 248, SY 36,
SY 347, SY 1235, UL 35, UL 51, UL 465,
WK 152, WK 1461, WY 47, WY 189

MORNING STAR Revelation 22:16
A 773, AH 84, BA 1, BA 124, BCK 10,
BCK 201, BF 50, BF 115, BF 319, BF 568,
BF 621, BF 625, BF 762, BF 818, BF 1130,
BF 1388, BF 1603, BF 1791, BK 255, BRD 138,
BRD 726, CY 11, CY 149, CY 231, FR 237,
FR 286, GU 34, GU 214, GU 325, KY 128,
LH 97, LH 250, LH 329, LK 627, LT 255
LT 315, ME 108, OB 426, PD 39, PD 122,
PD 234, SN 25, SY 13, SY 891, UL 286, WK 27,
WK 60, WK 332

NAOMI A 98, SN 124	Ruth 1:2
NARCISSUS A 606, LT 139	Romans 6:11
NAZARENE SS 114	Matthew 2:23
NIMROD BA 183, BF 371, BF 1028, BF 1034, INS 4, KY 75, KY 79, LH 115, LH 154	Genesis 10:9
NOON-TIDE KY 6, KY 163, KY 196, YH 33	Jeremiah 20:16
OLIVE BRANCH BF 339, BF 681, BF 1303, BK 300, GY 409, LH 38, LH 336, OB 233, PD 77, SY 95	Zechariah 4:12
OLIVE LEAF BCK 210, BCK 297, BF 1627, INS 54, INS 86, INS 128, KY 220, LH 43, PD 196, WK 457	Genesis 8:11
OLIVE TREE BA 127, FR 321, N 332	Psalms 52:8
ONE ACCORD LT 324	Acts 2:1
ONYX BF 1581, BK 295	Exodus 28:20
OPHIR BF 1871, BF 1923, GY 171	1 Kings 9:28
OPHIR LAND BF 131	1 Kings 9:28
ORION AH 83, B 184, BCK 69, BF 208, BF 368, BF 432, BF 703, BF 963, BF 985, BF 2039, E 72, INS 25, KY 118, KY 183, KY 352, LH 322, LK 304, N 384, PD 158, PZ 613	Job 9:9

PALESTINE	Joel 3:4
BF 1991, SN 240	
PARACLETE	John 14:16
KY ?	
PARVAIM	2 Chronicles 3:6
BF 123, BF 403	
PEACE BE STILL	Mark 4:39
BF 39, BF 514	
PILGRIM	Hebrews 11:13
AH 66, BF 270 , BF 400 , BF 1044 , BF 1109 ,	
FR 36, ME 607	
PLEIADES	Job 9:9
BF 155, BF 246, YH 227	
POMEGRANATE	Exodus 28:33
BF 1648	
PRESENT HELP	Psalms 46:1
FR 53, LT 1120	
QUIET WATERS	Psalms 23:2
B 436, FR 169, FR 253, GY 420, KY 309, LT 201,	
LT 279, ML 226, PD 20, PD 475, PD 589, PW 144,	
WK 12	
REDEEMED	1 Peter 1:18
SY 412	
REMEMBRANCE	Luke 22:19
AH ?, B 291, BF 43, CN 197, LH 174, LT 154,	
SY 297, WY 145	
ROSE OF SHARON	Song of Solomon 2:1
A 104, BF 25, BF 342, FR 23, LH 56,	
LH 247, LH 250, LT 529 , N 349 , PD 383,	
SS 118, WK 634	
ROYAL DIADEM	Isaiah 62:3
BA 10, BF 260, BK 121	

RUTH BF 535	Ruth 1:4
SAFFRON BA 172, BF 1859, INS 95, LH 120	Song of Solomon 4:14
SALEM BF 357, BF 492	Psalms 76:2
SAMARIAN GY 445	John 4:19
SAMARITAN GY 452, LT 407	Luke 10:33
SAMSON LO 304	Judges 13:24
SAPPHIRE BA 174, BF 322, BF 439, CN 35, CN 174, INS 391, LK 147, P 713, PD 285, SY 440, UL 194	Job 28:16
SAPPHIRE STONE BCK 304, BF 117, PD 185	Exodus 2:10
SARDIUS BF 985	Exodus 28:17
SAREPTA FR 207, LT 1021	Luke 4:26
SCARLET CORD BF 60, CH 59, DO 17, LH 334, LH 367	Joshua 2:18
SCARLET LINE LH 55	Joshua 2:18
SCARLET THREAD AH 139, B 397, BN ?, FR 328, KY 197, LH 209, LH 423, LK 713, PD 57	Joshua 2:18
SCEPTRE AH 10, BF 1650, K 44, LK 377, SY 78	Genesis 49:10

SHARON ROSE FR 400, LH 102, LH 119, LH 317, PD 182, PD 233, SY 182	Song of Solomon 2:1
SHELOMI A 466	Numbers 34:27
SHEMARIAH BF 499, BF 955, BF 1119, FR 245, N 124	1 Chronicles 12:5
SHEPHERD LAD FR 123, FR 215, GY 240, KY 216, LT 7	1 Samuel 17:34
SILVANUS BF 2056, LK 171	2 Corinthians 1:19
SILVER CHORD BA 62, FD ? KY 124, LK 179, PD 187, WK 488	Ecclesiastes 12:6
SILVER CORD AH 70, BCK 200, PD 437, SY 287	Ecclesiastes 12:6
SIMON PETER NN 83	Matthew 4:18
SOLOMON GY 372	2 Samuel 5:14
SPIKENARD BF 944	Mark 14:8
SPRINGING WELL BCK 255, BF 2054, SY 92	John 4:14
STAR DIVINE AH 449, BF 119, BK 47, LH 230, LH 449, PD 377, WK 16	Matthew 2:2
STAR OF BETHLEHEM B 331, BF 1655, BF 1948, CY 69, LH 400, ME 12, PD 96, PD 218, PD 527	Matthew 2:2

STAR OF HOPE A 411, BA 312, BA 374, BF 472, BF 1023, BF 1492, BK 28, CN 149, FR 34, KY?, LH 260, LH 274, LT 60, LT 225, N 288, PD 51	Matthew 2:2
(STAR OF HOPE) ASTRUM SPEI BF 57	Matthew 2:2
STAR OF PEACE A 304, A 370, LH 278, LT 74, M 133, PD 324, SH 143, WK 36, WK 150	Matthew 2:2
STAR OF PROMISE BF 402, FR 382, PD 70	Matthew 2:2
STAR OF THE EAST A 227, BF 113, BF 645, BF 719	Matthew 2:2
STEADFAST HOPE N 209, FR 43	Hebrews 6:19
STEPHANOS BF 1966	1 Corinthians 16:15
STILL WATERS LK 154	Psalms 23:2
SUZANNA BF 637, PZ 561	Luke 8:3
THESSALONIAN GY 112	1 Thessalonians 1:1
TOPAZ BCK 97, BF 52, BF 1645, BF 1822, LH 105	Exodus 28:17
TRUE FRIEND BF 109, LT 428	Proverbs 18:24
TRUE REWARD LT 172	Luke 6:35
TRUE TOKEN B 600, CN 298	Joshua 2:12

TRUE VINE	John 15:1
A 525, BF 199, BK 429, FR 97, FR 335,	
INS 565, KY 7, LH 31, ME 219, ML 20,	
N 176, PD 147, PD 349, RO 202, SY 522	
UPHAZ	Jeremiah 10:9
BF 823, BF 837	
VINE	1 Kings 4:25
BCK 412, BF 416, INS 31, PD 156	
VINTAGE	Job 24:6
BCK 380, BF 574	
VIRGIN	Isaiah 23:12
CN 68, CY 65, LH 429	
VIRGIN MARY	Isaiah 23:12
CY 282	
WAVE SHEAF	Leviticus 23:11
LK 172	
(THE) WAY	John 14:6
A 49, FD 268, FD 292	
WAYFARER	Isaiah 35:8
BA 377, BF 25, FR 190	
WELFARE	Nehemiah 2:10
B 163, BF 940, BK 137, FR 379, INS 77,	
LK 511	
WELLSPRING	Proverbs 16:22
BA 337, CN 207, FR 307, FR 406, LH 143	
ZABDI	Joshua 7:1
BF 1164	
ZAPHENATH - PANEA	Genesis 41:45
BCK 109, BF 2075	
ZARAH	Matthew 1:3
BF 1864	

ZEALOT LT 1104	Luke 6:15
ZEBULUN SH 105	Genesis 30:20
ZIMRI BF 665, BF 683	1 Kings 16:5

The names in this section may not strictly be classed as Biblical, but they are linked with the principles and teachings of the Holy Scriptures.

ABSTAINER
BF 176, BF 302, BF 347, BF 1178, BF 1768, BF 2063

AMAZING GRACE
B 202, CN 289

BE GRACEFUL
B 232

BE IN TIME
BCK 393, BF 114, BF 284, BF 1554, ML 275

BRIGHT REWARD
LH 93, LH 234

BRIGHTER DAWN
KY 658, LK 47, LH 219, PD 62, PD 295, RO 5

BRIGHTER MORN
CN 72, CN 151, LK 239, PD 339

CELESTIAL DAWN
FR 392

CHRISTMAS
PH 62

CLOUDLESS MORN
B 176

DAILY BREAD
LT 269

FAITHFUL AGAIN
BF 267

FEAR NOT
BCK 9, BF 25, BF 120, BF 752, BRD 311, INS 197, LK 644, LT 497, PD 81, SY 273

FELLOWSHIP
BF 281, FR 241, FR 400, LT 65, LT 246

FLOWING STREAM
BF 12, BF 395

FORERUNNER
LT 1160

FRUITFUL HARVEST
A281, DO 67, PD 47, PD 247

GLORY
LT 1027

GOLDEN DAWN
B 153, BA 230, BRD 133, BS 78, CK 299, CN 119, FR 317, LH 184, N 1,
PD 211, PD 239, PD 255, RO 50

GOOD FRIDAY
LH 10

GOOD WAY
FR 330

GRACIOUS
FR 167

GRATITUDE
A 689, BCK 252, BF 928, FR 249, INS 272, LH 28, LK 173, ML 17, PD 143,
RO 19

GUIDE ME
BK 16, FR 915, FY 233, INS 254, LK 106, WK 173

HOPE
BCK 59, BCK 363, BF 402, BK 82, BRD 79, CY 15, CY 17, KY 136,
KY 167, LH 146, LK 102, LK 241, LK 284, LK 380, PD 96

JOHN WESLEY
BF 35, BF 430, FH 88, FY 35

JOSEPH AND MARY
GY 1323

KINDLY LIGHT
BK 241

LEAD ME
FR 23, FY 382

LILY OF ISRAEL
CY 75

MARTIN LUTHER
BF 1095

MARY SLESSOR
BF 1803

MISSIONARY
BF 20

MORNING SONG
FR 402

NEW KIRK
BF 6

PALM TREE
BF 320, FR 43

PEACE
PD 130

PIETY
WY 168

PILOT ME
BF 392, SH 245, WY 12

RADIANT WAY
BK 210, FR 22, FR 234, FR 329, LH 147

RAPTURE
BF 27

ROCK OF AGES
BK 172

SHARON VALE
BF 192, LH 304

SHINING LIGHT
B 113

STAR OF FAITH
LH 77, N 137, PD 160, UL 228

ST ABBS
SN 208

ST ACHILLEUS
H 215

ST ADRIAN
KY 202, KY 245

ST AETHANS
INS 86

ST AGNES
FD 6, SN 88

ST AIDAN
HL 89, ME 69

ST ALCUIN
H 125

ST ALEXANDER
H 373

ST AMANDUS
H 247, H 505

ST AMANT
H 42, H 702, SH 38

ST ANDREW
A 787, CY 62, CY 406, H 18, LT 335, SY ?

ST ANDRONICUS
H 241

ST ANTHONY
B 194

ST APOLLO
H 592

ST ARCADIUS
H 207

ST ATTALUS
H 167

ST AUSLEM
CY 247

ST AYLES
KY 122

ST BARTHOLOMEW
FD 27

ST BENEDICT
CN 47, GY 592, H 164

ST BERNHARD
CN 276

ST BOTOLPH
CN 8

ST BRELADE
H 64

ST BRIDE
CY 390, CY 391, GU 211

ST BRIDGET
CY 169

ST BRITWIN
GY 295, H 124

ST CATHERINE
CN 127, LH 90

ST CELESTIN
H 192, H 233

ST CHAD
H 120

ST CHRISTOPHER
BN 19, LT 340

ST CLAIR
BA 8, BF 147, BF 152, BF 299, BF 360, BF 499, BF 674, FD 15,
GY 387, LH 53, LK 250, PZ 199

ST CLAIRS
CY 5, LH 53

ST CLAUDE
LT 714

ST CLEMENT
A 70

ST CLOUD
GY 856

ST COLUMBA
CY 49, CY 52

ST COMBS
FR 298, FR 367, GY 11

ST COMBS HAVEN
FR 81

ST CROIX
LT 251

ST DELPHINE
H 380

ST DOMINIC
H 116

ST DONATS
H 35

ST EBBA
BK 210

ST ELMO
H 606

ST ELSTAN
H 484

ST ENDELLION
LO 115

ST GATIEN
H 189

ST GEORGE
LN 73, LT 59, LT 402

ST GERARDINE
INS 251

ST GERONTIUS
H 69, H 350

ST GILES
H 220, H 350

ST GOTHARD
GN 46

ST HILDA
HL 50

ST HONORIUS
H 66

ST HUBERT
H 49

ST IGNATIUS
CY 408

ST IRENE
H 472

ST ISABELLE
PH 15

ST IVES
CY 81

ST JAMES
CY 304, LT 492

ST JASON
H 436

ST JASPER
H 31

ST JEROME
H 442

ST JOAN
H 450

ST JOHN
H 254, KY 15, LT 7

ST JOSEPH
CY 338, N 263

ST JULIAN
CN 326

ST JUST
H 320, LO 434

ST KENAN
H 360

ST KENTCHERILL
CY 290

ST KEVERNE
H 158, H 340, GY 445

Morning Star FR 286

THE PRUNIER TROPHY
The crew of the Portsoy steam drifter *Boy Andrew*, BF 592, at the
presentation of the Prunier Trophy in London in 1936.
Left to right:-
James Bruce; David McKay; Alex McKay; Wm. Mair; Andrew Mair, (the
boy Andrew); Joe Mair, (skipper); George Addison; John Morrison;
John McKay.

Cornucopia FR 129
Admiralty name *Cloud*

Remembrance

Boy Andrew, BF 592 entering Great Yarmouth.
Admiralty name, *Sunburst*

Mizpah BF 57

Deliverer BF 67

Golden Bells BF 130 leaving Macduff

ST KILDA
BA 137, H 355,

ST LAWRENCE
SN 102

ST LEANDER
H 420

ST LEGER
H 178, H 482

ST LEONARD
SN 217

ST LOLAN
H 139

ST LOMAN
H 156, H 381

ST LUCIA
H 937, LT 362,

ST LUCY
CY 136

ST LUKE
LT 132, LT 156

ST MAGNUS
LH 179

ST MARGARET
CY 177

ST MARGUERITE
SE 68, TH 91

ST MARK
CY 95, H 152, LT 327

ST MARTIN
LT 376

ST MATTHEW
H 201, H 284

ST MARY
CN 223, CN 274, CN 300, CY 21, CY 22, CY 168, CY 380

ST MAUGHOLD
DO 24

ST MEL
LT 12

ST MELANTE
GY 80, H 367

ST MERRYN
GY 84, H 40

ST MICHAEL
CY 422

ST MINIVER
GY 458

ST MUNGO
GN 90

ST NECTAN
H 411

ST NEOTS
H 112

ST NICHOLAS
LH 113

ST NICOLA
LT 83

ST NINIAN
CY 55, LH 386

ST OLIVE
SN 47

ST OSWALD
H 335

ST PATRICK
CY 48

ST PETER
CY 8, CY 234, CY 292, CY 381, CY 426, H 102, LT 338, N 306

ST PHILIP
FD 199

ST PHILLIP
LT 144

ST PIERRE
BM 180

ST REMY
J 278

ST ROMANUS
H 223, H 426

ST ROSE
LT 82, LT 300, H 492

ST SEBASTIAN
H 470

ST SIMON
LT 304

ST STANISLAS
PW 149

ST STEPHEN
H 299, LY 82

ST SYLVERE
J 437

ST THERESA
CY 4, CY 409

ST THOMAS
LT 8

ST VALERY
H 691

ST VINCENT
CY 405, H 933, LT 123, LT 272, WK 117

ST WILFRED OF SELSEY
LI 6

ST WINIFRED
CY 45, CY 420, WK 88

ST WISTAN
H 486

ST ZENO
H 255

TRUST ON
BF 1050

WESLEY
BK 273

XMAS MORN
BF 102, FR 31, FR 218

XMAS STAR
BK 103, FR 87

THE 'STANDARD' BOATS

During World War 1, (1914-19), the Admiralty built a number of steam drifters for use as minesweepers and tenders. These were built to specification and were known as 'standard' boats. When hostilities ceased the drifters were sold to the fishermen for herring and line fishing. The names given to the boats by the Admiralty were related, directly or indirectly, to the elements.

Most fishermen changed the names according to their own preference although some kept the Admiralty name throughout their sea-going years.

Abbreviations:- S. steel-built; W. wooden.

ADMIRALTY NAMES		LATER NAMES
Afterglow	W	Port Richard, sold to the Falkland Islands
Airpocket	W	Ambitious GY 51, Cineraria GY 51.
Anticyclone	W	never fished
Astral	W	never fished
Atmosphere	W	Atmosphere H 797, GY 45.
Avalanche	W	Lochalsh INS 221.
Backwash	W	Morven Hill WK 83, William G. Farrow H464
Black Frost	W	Mill Water FR 81.
Black Night	W	Black Night GY 188.
Blare	S	May Bird LT 449.
Blizzard	S	Satinstone H 585, Harvest Gleaner FR 73, BF 48
Blue Haze	S	Blue Haze LT 564, Jean Baird PD 1.

Blue Sky	W	never fished
Bluster	W	Helen West BF 84, Sergius GY ?, Fertility PD 147
Borealis	W	Brash GY 119
Bow Wave	S	Bow Wave LT 589, Lilium PD 67.
Breaker	S	Kathleen LT 673
Brine	S	Brine BCK 246, GY 85.
Broil	S	Broil LT 610, M.A. West FR 240.
Bubble	S	Bubble LT 372, Unicity R 22.
Calm	S	John Hedley SN 35, Pre-eminent INS 55 , FR 173, YH 91.
Cascade	S	Illustrious PD 187.
Catspaw	S	never fished
Chimera	S	J . R. Mitchell PD 448, Twinkling Star PD 448, KY 347 .
Cirrus	W	Traveller's Joy.
Clearing	S	Clearing PD 197, Vernal BF 525 , PD 239 .
Cloud	S	Cornucopia FR 129, Protect Me PD 209.
Cold Blast	S	Cold Blast PD 195, Elsie Bruce BF 53.
Cold Snap	S	Cold Snap A111, Whitehill PD 390.
Conflagration	S	Conflagration LT 620, Jacklyn LT 327
Crescent Moon	S	never fished
Cumulus	W	Boy Jermyn GY 105.

Current	S	Current LO ? Copious KY 175, Ocean Hunter YH 296, LT 322
Cyclone	S	Cyclone LT 737
Dawn	S	Jane Wright LT 732
Daybreak	S	Ralph Hall Caine YH 447, Allochy FR 124, LT 109.
Daylight	W	Tradewind BF 575 .
Dayspring	W	Castlebay FD 377, Hazelglen BCK 145.
Darkness	W	Sea Holly PD 158.
Dew	S	Dew A 361, Moyra INS 586, Olive Tree FR 321, Calm Waters LT 407
Distance	S	Leonard Boyle SN 45, Dundarg FR 212, Excel IV, LT 171
Doldrum	W	Beatrice Eves LT 921, Gloamin FR 96.
Drizzle	S	Pilot Star LT 1040, KY 48 , FR 106 , PD 200
Dusk	S	Dusk PZ ?, Cosmea KY 21 , Coredalis KY 21
Falling Star	S	Falling Star LT 263, Betty Bodie BCK 400, PD 304
Fair Wind	S	Hawthorn Bank BK 163, LT 237, Jacketa LT 237
Fairweather	W	Fairweather PD 603
Fiery Cross	W	Fircroft GY 242
Fire Bell	W	Maviston INS 184, Hollydale FR 171, BF 70
Firelight	W	Just Reward LT 592.

Firmament	W	Firmament FR 242, Foxglove PD 593.
Flaff	S	Flaff BCK 359, River Ugie BF 74, Nellie Gardiner BF 74.
Flame	W	Uberous KY 62, PD 269.
Flash	S	A.T.A. GY 309
Flat Calm	W	Rowan Tree BF 199.
Fleck	W	Fleck LT 599, M 240.
Flicker	S	Mary Watt FR 217, Sea Reaper PD 396.
Floodtide	W	Marjorie Grace LT 491.
Flotsam	W	Flotsam LT 592, GY 137.
Flow	S	Flow GY 18, BCK 436, PD 291.
Flurry	W	Flurry INS 252, Gleam On PD 37.
Flush	W	Flush INS 177, KY 184, FD 43.
Flutter	W	Golden Sunbeam YH 279.
Foam	S	Starwort LH ?, Menat KY 232, Plough KY 232
Fog Bank	W	Dyker Lassie KY 75, Rennyhill KY 75.
Fog Bow	W	Fertile Vale BF 52, FR 103.
Fog Break	S	Craoghall LH 383, Spes Aurea KY 81, LT 52, PD 49
Fork Lightning	S	Ramsey Bay FD 378, LT 1290.
Fountain	W	Whitenight GY 38.
Freshet	S	Xmas Rose FR 531, Jean Paterson A ?
Froth	S	Florence Pritchard LI ?, Manx Princess DO 91, Eunice & Nellie BCK 118, PD 309.

Full Moon	W	Rosehaugh INS 20, BF 98 .
Fumarole	S	Fumarole PD 367.
Fume	S	Fume LT 425.
Galaxy	S	Galaxy LT 417.
Gale	S	Ocean Lover YH 105, PD 157.
Glacier	W	Girl Joey LK 66, Silver Sky PD 41.
Gleam	W	Douglas BK ?, Reids PD 189.
Glint	W	Glint BCK 352, Prospects Ahead PD 256.
Glitter	S	Ocean Raleigh PD 139.
Gloaming	W	never fished.
Gloss	S	Gloss LT 528, Murielle LT 269.
Glow	S	Glow LT 688
Greek Fire	W	Greek Fire FR 89, Paradigm FR 89, BK 145
Green Sea	S	Gladys & Violet A 639, Riant INS 30 .
Grey Sea	S	Grey Sea BM 211, LT 1279, BCK 184, Rosebay PD 65, BF 69, YH 68.
Groundswell	S	Elie Ness LT 1259, Trusty Star LT 1259.
Gulf Stream	S	Gulf Stream LT 601, SN 42, Jenny Irvin SN 21, LT 57.
Gust	S	Burnhaven PD 589, BCK 73, LT 196.
Hailstorm	W	Hailstorm LK 173, Girl Lizzie LK 173 , Goss Water LK 173
Halo	S	Halo SA 121.
Harmattan	S	Harmattan PD 399, Wellspring PD 399.

Heatwave	W	Heatwave GY 1296.
High Tide	S	High Tide LT 700.
Horizon	S	Hamnavoe FR 123, Amaranth YH 117.
Hurricane	W	Hurricane R 90, Charde R 90.
Iceberg	S	Iceberg LT 622, Marigold INS 478, PD 81, PD 124
Iceblink	W	Star Divine PD 377.
Icefield	S	Jessie Watson KY 52, Anster Belle KY 52, Memoria KY 52, Unity BCK 109, Ocean Unity YH 293.
Iceflow	S	Icefloe LT 723.
Icepack	S	Icepack LT 1244, Accord LT 1244, Ocean Sunbeam YH 344.
Icicle	S	Mildred W. Rawson LO ?, June Rose PD 592.
Imbat	W	Imbat BCK 384, PD 105.
Indian Summer	S	Indian Summer A 342.
Iridescence	W	never fished.
Landbreeze	S	Landbreeze A 315, LT 1296.
Landfall	S	never fished.
Lasher	S	Lasher KY 25, BF 79, LT 408, Golden Ring LT 408.
Leeward	S	Betty Duthie FR 207, Lustre PD 201.
Levanter	S	never fished.
Lop	W	Greynight GY 141.

Low Tide	S	Low Tide LT 725, Seaward GY ?, Mary Flett INS ?, Loyal Friend LT 725.
Lull	S	Lull B 38, Eunelma BCK 438, Myrtle Leaf PD 102, Marshal Pak LT 400.
Lunar Bow	S	Lunar Bow PD 245.
Mackerel Sky	W	Drainie INS 315, Headway FR 39.
Maelstrom	W	Maelstrom GY 15, Fair Haven PD 216
Melody	S	Rose Duncan BCK 122, SH 105, Lord Duncan LT 273.
Midnight Sun	W	never fished.
Milky Way	W	Milky Way BF 366, Boyds FR 294.
Mirage	S	Thorntree LH?, Mary & Jane BK?, Jackora LT 129.
Mist	S	James Johnston BF 101, Cairnmor PD 375, Welcome Boys LT ?
Mistral	W	Golden Line LT 619.
Moonbeam	S	Skimmer GY 7.
Moonlight	W	Carry On LT 583.
Moonrise	W	Moonrise LT 1003, Ascendant YH 35.
Moonset	S	Flora Taylor PD 444, LT 239.
Moonshine	S	never fished.
Morn	S	Homefinder LH ?, Bene Vertat KY 208, Defensor KY 208, PD 185.
Murk	S	Girl's Friend LT 173, Trust PD 243.
Nadir	W	Salpha PH ?

Neaptide	S	Neaptide A?, Smiling Thru LT?
Nebula	S	Nacre A 410. Sea Toiler BCK 14, Calliopsis KY 223, LT 92.
New Moon	S	The Milnes PD 202, Ugievale PD 202.
Nightfall	W	Nightfall H 317.
Nimbus	W	Girl Bella GY 1292, Netsam GY 1292
Node	S	Tiger's Eye H 577, GY 60, Lossie INS 125, Golden View FR 44, PD 23.
Noontide	S	Noontide KY 6, KY 196, YH 33.
Northern Lights	S	Sunnyside Girl LT 415.
Ocean Swell	S	Ocean Swell LT 1210, YH 471.
Outline	S	Outline LY 1211, Inspiration LT 1211, Norbreeze LT ?
Overfall	S	Overfall BF 590, LT 76.
Ozone	S	Girl Georgia LK 152, Margaret West FR ?
Packice	W	Murray Clan INS 314, Utilise PD 17.
Pampero	S	Edalba YH 218, Acorn KY 194, LT 31.
Phase	W	Phase PD 197, INS 301, BCK 91.
Phosphorous	S	Ocean Sprite YH 56, PD 94.
Puff	S	Puff LY 1106, Gowanhill FR 39.
Quicksand	S	Quicksand A 394, PD 5, Ephratah PD 170.
Radiation	S	Radiation KY 185, Agnes Gardner KY 185, PD 395.
Rainbrand	S	Craiglea INS 540, YH 81.

Rainstorm	W	Rainstorm LO 527.
Ray	W	Margaret & Francis LH 188.
Red Sky	W	Red Sky PD 25, BCK 387.
Refraction	W	Refraction FR 243, BF 412.
Reverberation	W	Reverberation LT 239.
Rift	W	Doonie Braes INS 344.
Rime	W	Rime BF 440, PD 166.
Rising Sea	W	Rising Sea LO 526, BCK 110.
Runnel	W	Runnel GY 1266, GN 132.
Sandstorm	S	Glenbreck A 381, River Eye BK 3, Olden Times BK 3, Season's Gift LT 127
Scend	W	Girl Hazel PH ? William Woolven PH ?
Scintilla	S	Asparagus LH ? Mary Swanston BK 446.
Scour	W	Cheviotdale BK 427.
Scud	W	Fluerbaix LT 422.
Seabreeze	S	Sapphire Stone BF 117.
Shade	W	Shade GY 186.
Shadow	W	Shadow WK 177, PD 219, Pilot Us ?
Sheen	S	Good Tidings PD 246, Summer Rose PD 246.
Sheet Lightning	W	Sheet Lightning PD 99, Roseacre BF 479.
Shimmer	W	Shimmer LO 524.
Shooting Stars	W	Shooting Stars BCK 57.
Shower	S	Shower All?

Silhouette	W	Honora Evelyn FD 165.
Silt	W	Silt INS 84, Rosevalley INS 84.
Sirocco	W	Cat's Eye H 316 .
Skyline		never fished.
Sleet	S	Sleet SN 47, Eyedale BK 5, PD 75, Consolation BK 5, Fairhaven KY 713 .
Snowdrift	W	Fife Ness A 522, KY 27, George G. Baird PD 256.
Snowflake	S	Mary Herd FR 24, A 570.
Solstice	W	Solstice INS 276.
Spate	W	Spate H 326, Marguerite H 326 .
Spectrum	S	Spectrum WK 217, BF 196, PD 73.
Splash	W	Space H 293 .
Spurt	S	Craigentinny PD 185, FR 567.
Squall	W	Squall BCK 399, Golden Feather FR 11.
Starlight	W	Starlight PD 21, Starlight Rays PD 21.
St. Elmo's Light	W	St Elmo's Light BCK 354, Sweet Promise PD 385.
Sternwave	S	Craigleith LH 255, Summer Rose PD 594.
Stormcentre	W	Stormcentre GY 875, North Haven PD 164.
Stormwrack	W	Stormwrack FR 110, Perillia?
Sunburst	S	Boy Andrew BF 592.
Sundown	S	Zena & Ella BCK ?, Mace KY 224, LT 35.

Sunlight	W	Hannah Taylor GY 1193, Snowstorm GY 1193.
Sunshine	S	Craigroy FR 251, BF 81.
Sunspot	W	Sunspot INS 317, Mary Johnston ?
Sunrise	W	Sunrise LT 621 , Taal Hina?, Scania LT?, Tillyduff FR 190.
Sunset	S	never fished
Surge	W	Surge LT 487, Resurge LT 487, YH 21.
Swell	W	Silvernight GY 138.
Swirl	W	Swirl GY 189.
Thaw	W	Thaw INS 176, Olive Leaf PD 196.
Thunderbolt	W	Ina Adams GY 7, Midnight Sun GY 7, PD 39, Green Pastures FR 72.
Thunderclap	S	never fished.
Tidal Range	W	Tidal Range GY 403.
Tidal Wave	S	Tidal Wave BF 200, Sophia S. Summers PD? Norman Wilson KY 228.
Tiderip	W	Kentish Belle R ?
Tropic	W	never fished.
Twinkle	W	Cloudarch GY 187.
Typhoon	S	Ocean Lassie YH 78.
Undertow	S	Undertow BCK 368, Spes Melior KY 19.
Vapour	W	Vapour LT 1088, Xmas Eve BF 76, FR 68.
Volume	W	Go Ahead LT 534.

Waft	S	Genius BCK 358, FR 299.
Waterfall	S	Homocea YH 214, Sedulous LT 112.
Watershed	S	Watershed LT 628, Salvian GY ? Convallaria BF 479, BF 51, BF 106
Watersmeet	S	George Baker YH 210, LY 1253.
Wavelet	S	Ocean Dawn YH 47.
Whirlblast	S	Stella Aurora KY 45, FR 54, Jackora LT 116, Abiding Friend LT 116.
Whirlpool	S	Whirlpool A ?
White Horses	S	Benachie A 301, FR 15, A 568.
Whitecloud	S	Admiral Startin LH ?, Fisher Lad BF 204
Will o' the Wisp	W	"Waterway", Bristol, never fished
Willwaw	S	Willwaw BM 207, Moray Rose INS 101, PD 97
Windfall	S	Windfall INS 189, SY 567
Windhowl	W	Harnser LT 627
Windrise	S	Windrise A 291, Quiet Waters PD 589
Windshift	S	Windshift A 463, Cassiopea KY 14, LT 86, PD 34
Windwall	W	Plumer LT 596
Windward	S	Windward BCK 349, Coulit Head PD ? Scarlet Thread PD 57

THE PRUNIER TROPHY

The first winners.

It was on the 5th of November, 1936, while drift-net fishing on the Haisbro' Grounds off East Anglia, that the crew of the Portsoy steam drifter, Boy Andrew, BF 592, hauled in a herring catch, which, when landed at Great Yarmouth, totalled 231 crans.

The usual 'fleet' of nets operated by the steam drifter was 80, so the average per net in this case was about 3 crans, a weight of around 9 cwts.

This 'shot' proved to be the highest catch of that season, and won the Prunier Trophy the first year it was awarded.

The trophy was gifted by a French lady, Madame Simone Prunier, to be awarded to the boat with the highest catch at Lowestoft and Great Yarmouth, during October and November of the East Anglian season.

The prize included a marble trophy, to be displayed at the winner's hometown for the ensuing year, a weather-vane for the ship's mast-head, and, for the crew, an all-expenses-paid trip to London where the trophy was presented.

It was on display, 1936-1937, in the window of the grocery shop on Church Street, Portsoy, which was owned by Mr. George Wood.

There was an annual award from 1936 to 1966, with the exception of the years of World War 2, and the year 1965, when there was no presentation.

The crew of the Boy Andrew at the presentation in 1936 were:-
James Bruce; David McKay; Alex McKay; William Mair; Andrew Mair (the boy Andrew); Joe Mair (skipper); George Addison; John Morrison; John Mckay.

The Prunier Trophy:- the subsequent winners.

LT 47	PEACE WAVE
LT 167	HOSANNA
LT 89	PRESENT FRIENDS
YH 63	ROMANY ROSE
LT 178	PATRIA
LT 371	DAUNTLESS STAR
LT 276	HERRING SEARCHER
YH 105	WYDALE
PD 218	STAR OF BETHLEHEM
LT 20	LORD HOOD
PD 147	FRUITFUL BOUGH
LK 509	JESSIE SINCLAIR
PD 234	MORNING STAR
LT 46	SILVER CREST
FR 156	STEPHENS
KY 124	SILVER CHORD
LT 156	ST.LUKE
LT 367	DAUNTLESS STAR
FR 178	SILVER HARVEST
LT 61	DICK WHITTINGTON
YH 61	OCEAN STARLIGHT
LT 137	NORFOLK YEOMAN
LT 671	SUFFOLK WARRIOR
FR 346	TEA ROSE

FURTHER READING

The stock of Aberdeen City Libraries includes numerous books, articles and illustrative items relating to the Scottish fishing industry, past and present.

The following will be of particular interest to those who wish to read more about the way of life, religion and traditions of north-east fisherfolk.

Abbreviations indicate departments of the Central Library where items are available for loan or consultation:-

C.L.   Central Lending Library - item available for loan.
Comm.   Commercial Library - item available for loan
R. Lo.   Local Studies Library - item available for consultation.
R.   Reference Library - item available for consultation.
C.J.   Children's Library - item available for loan.

ANSON, Peter
Fisher folk-lore.
Faith Press, 1965
An account of old customs, taboos and superstitions among fisher folk, especially in Brittany and Normandy and on the east coast of
Scotland.   C.L.   398.3
                                            R. Lo.   398.3

ANSON, Peter F
Scots fisherfolk
Banffshire Journal, 1950
An account of social background, customs and religious attitudes of fisherfolk with sections on fishing stations, fishing methods and types
of vessels.   Comm.   639.20941
                                            R.Lo.   639.20941

BOCHEL, Margaret
Dear Gremista; the story of Nairn fisher girls at the gutting.
National Museum of Antiquities of Scotland, 1979
This account of living and working conditions refers particularly to the fishing at Lerwick and is illustrated by numerous photographs and
drawings.   R.   P639.22

BUCHAN, A.R.
Fishing out of Peterhead.
Aberdeen and North East Scotland Family History Society, 1986.
Based on a talk given to the Society, this pamphlet explores the sources
which are available for the study of Peterhead whaling, herring fishing
and white fishing.   R.Lo.   P639.22

BUTCHER, D.
Following the fishing; the days when bands of Scots fisher girls
followed the herring fleets round Britain...
Tops'l Books, 1987.
An oral history record of fisher girls, netmakers, coopers, boat-builders,
and other craftsmen who kept the fleets at sea and dealt with the catch.
                                                      R. Lo.   639.2755
                                                      C. L.   301.4443

CRANNA, John
Fisher life in Buchan; a series of articles on fisher life, customs and
superstitions which appeared in the *Bon-Accord and Northern Pictorial*,
from 27th February to 27th March, 1931.
                                                      R.Lo.   P639.22

DRUMMOND, James
Get up and tie your fingers.
In *Scots Magazine*, November 1981, pp. 165-173
Reminiscences of Scots fisher lasses who followed the herring fleet from
port to port and whose job was to gut and pack the herring.
                                                      R.   052 SC03
                                                      R.Lo.   P639.22

DUTHIE, John Lowe
The Fishermen's religious revival.
In *History Today*, December, 1983 pp. 22-27
The Revival of 1921 as a consequence of industrial crisis.
                                                      R.   905 H62
                                                      R.Lo.   P639.22

GLIMMER OF COLD BRINE
A Scottish sea anthology, edited by Alistair Laurie, Hellen Matthews
and Douglas Ritchie.
Aberdeen University Press in association with Grampian Regional
Council, 1988.
This collection of prose and verse shows the influence of the sea on the

lives and thoughts of fisherfolk, adventurers, smugglers and oilmen. It contains extracts from the works of Scottish writers, past and present, well-known and obscure, illustrated by reproductions of paintings and photographs.   C.L.   Lo.828.9941
                                                          R. Lo.   828.9941

GRAHAM, Cuthbert
Portrait of the Moray Firth
Hale, 1977
Includes descriptions and historical details of the cliff-foot and cliff-top fishing communities from Fraserburgh to Wick.
                                                          C.L.   914.1
                                                          R.   914.1

HUTCHESON, George
Days of yore; Buckie and district in the past.
Banffshire Advertiser, 1887
Chapters 6 - 9 deal with the superstitions and customs observed in the fishing stations at Buckie, Portgordon, Findochty and Portknockie.
                                                          R.Lo.   941.24

LEATHAM, James
Fisherfolk of the North-East
Deveron Press, Turriff, (1932)
Anecdotes of fisher life are interspersed with descriptions of traditional festivities and religious attitudes. There are useful chapters on the use of tee-names and diminutives and on Peterhead at the height of the herring fishing season.   R.Lo.   914.125

MCGIBBON, John
The Fisherfolk of Buchan; a true story of Peterhead.
Marshall, 1922
This account of habits, beliefs and traditions includes lengthy chapters on the Revival of 1859-60 and on the special quality of the Sabbath day.
                                                          R.Lo.   914.125

MACLEAN, Charles
The Fringe of gold; the fishing villages of Scotland's east coast, Orkney and Shetland.
Canongate Publishing, 1985
Describes the special features, history and traditions of East Coast ports and fishing stations from the Borders to the North.
                                                          C.L.   914.12
                                                          R.Lo.   941

MARSHALL, Michael
Fishing; the coastal tradition
Batsford 1987
A descriptive and photographic record of life among the British Coastal
fisherfolk of the 1980s.   Comm.   639.22

RITCHIE, Jackie
Floods upon the dry ground.
Peterhead Offset, 1983.
The spiritual awakening among the fisherfolk of North-east Scotland
and East Anglia, 1921-23.   C.L   Lo.266.02
                                             R.Lo.   266.022

SCOTCH fisher life, as it was and is.
In *Chambers' Journal*, 22nd July 1899, pp. 541-544.
Life in the villages of Cairnbulg, Inverallochy and St. Combs in the
1840s.   R.   052 C35

SCOTT, James
A description of seafaring life on the North-east coast of Scotland
including the Moray Firth.
Aberdeen Journal, 1879
An account of the adversities of the fisherman's life with notes on
fishing stations from Aberdeen to Wick.   R.Lo.   P639

SLATER, James
A seafaring saga gleaned from the good old days.
Commercial Fishing Enterprises, 1979.
This anthology of personal memories, verse and prose includes
chapters on fisher weddings, superstitions and the Revival 1921-23.
                                             C.L.   Lo.639.22
                                             R. Lo.   639.22

SUTHERLAND, Iain
From herring to seine net fishing on the east coast of Scotland.
Camps Bookshop, Wick, (1985).
An investigation of the way in which seine netting replaced traditional
methods of fishing. Illustrated with numerous photographs, drawings
and diagrams.   C.L.   639.220
                                             R.Lo.   639.22

TAYLOR, James
Fishing the North East; a guide to the places, the people and their craft.
Northern Books, 1988.
Notes on the fishing communities from Whinnyfold to Sandend and on
fisher life and customs.   R. Lo.   639.22
                                  C. L.   639.20941

THOMPSON, Paul and others
Living the fishing
Routledge, 1983
The impact of economic and technological change through the last
hundred years on the fisher way of life in Scotland and East Anglia.
                                  Comm.   639.22
                                  R. Lo.   639.22

The Local Studies Library also contains a collection of approximately 1000
photographs of Scottish fishing vessels, ranging from early steam herring
drifters to the more modern motor trawlers. The nucleus of this useful
resource is the *Benzie Collection* which was purchased in the early 1970s and
which depicts mainly vessels sailing from the ports of north-east Scotland
from the 1920s to the 1960s.

Further information on the Prunier Trophy and its winners is contained in
the under-noted book, available for loan from the Commercial and Technical
Department of Aberdeen City Libraries:-

HAWKINS, L.W.
The Prunier Herring Trophy.
Port of Lowestoft Research Society, 1982.   Comm.   639.2755

A NOTE TO NESSIE

Ye great deceivin' feckless beast,
We're a' confused, tae say the least;
Hidin' in yon watery den
And jist appearin' noo and then.

A hunner times I've sailed Loch Ness,
But oh, alas, I maun confess,
I've never seen yer face nor form;
Though I've come thru in calm and storm.

Noo are ye jist a phantom wraith?
Male or female, or jist baith?
For this is evolution's notion
We cam' fae jeely in the ocean.
I'm nae deceived, for weel I ken,
When oor God made the world o' men
O ilka kind He made a pair,
That each the ither's life would share:
But did He mak' ye jist yersel'?
Noo will ye please my doobts dispel.

But then if ye are really there,
Tak' my advice, tak' heed, beware;
The Japs cam' ower tae search yer haunt,
.   And that was jist a worthless jaunt;
But noo the Yanks are on yer trail
I am gey sure their stunt will fail:
For I can see this is their plan
Tae tak' ye aff tae Disney-lan';
They'll pit yer photie in the papers
And mak' a film o' a' yer capers,
Then tie ye wi' a chine and collar
Tae further boost the mighty dollar;
So watch yer step, guard every move,
Lest they should your existence prove
'Cause for this purpose ye were made,
Tae boost auld Scotia's toorist trade.

(Published in *Aberdeen Press & Journal*, December 17th, 1975, the writer's
name being given as James Slater, Portsoy)

A REPLY FROM NESSIE

Dear J.S.P. I read yer note,
I got the 'Journal' aff a boat;
A Banffie that was passin' by,
On passage tae the Isle o' Skye.

I will yer every doobt dispel,
For I am here, alive and well:
Ye see yon ripple? Weel, that's me,
Or that great, crookit, floatin' tree,
Syne may-be shaddas fae the hills
That gie some glaiket toorists thrills;
Ye need a drap o' Heilan' Brew,
For that improves the distant view.

My origin, I canna' tell,
But I'm gey langsome here masel';
I wouldna mind a handsome mate
Tae share my lane aquatic state.

There was a lot o' folks cam' here,
Wi' ships, and underwater gear;
'Twas them had stuff that knocked me stupid,
I hae heard tell 'twas made by Cupid:
And wi' a box and flashin' licht,
They nearly took awa' my sicht;
I watch them weel, so dinna fear,
I'll nae let them come ower near,
I will aye boost yer toorist trade,
But I would need a kilt, and plaid,
A tartan tammy, and a sporran
Tae greet the guests, baith hame and foreign:

Ye want tae ken jist hoo I look,
So ye can write it in a book;
I hae a heid weel oot at front
A body like an upturned punt,
Usefa' flippers, but nae sail
And one great, interestin' TALE.

NESSIE, Glen-euchart, Loch Ness

(Published in *Aberdeen Press & Journal*, December 18th, 1975)

ON WORKING TO RULE

Men devise a book o' rules,
    as plain as they can be
Tae let their servants richtly ken
    what they're required tae dee;
But when the men obey the book
    and strictly heed the rules,
The job gangs wrang, production fa's,
    the boss then raves and scools.

If it be wrang tae dee what's richt
    I canna' understand
The folly that devised a' this,
    or yet the system planned:
For laws are kept, or broken,
    they winna boo nor bend,
Tae suit the whims o' them that seek,
    tae gain a selfish end.

But turnin' fae the ways o' men,
    tae ways that are divine;
There is anither Book o' rules
    whaur truth and honour shine;
Contained therein a code o' life,
    once ca'ed the 'Golden Rule',
Its sacred principles I learnt,
    when but a bairn at school:
Nae loose interpretation,
    or double standards here,
But what is noo required o' me
    set oot richt stracht and clear.
Oor nation's problems would be solved,
    and justice would be done;
If we would heed the rule that's found,
    in Luke 6:31.

LEARNING TO WRITE

My first attempt at writin'
    was wi' 'scally' and a slate;
The venue was the Ramsay School,*
    the year was nineteen eight.
And if when addin' two and two
    the answer wasna' richt,
I had a clootie that I used
    and ga'ed the slate a dicht.

A pencil and some paper cam',
    as writin' skills improved;
As on the education scale
    aye further on I moved:
A rubber was gey handy then
    but gar't the teacher rage,
For when the spellin' I would change,
    the rubber siled the page.

Syne I got a copy book,
    it was the standard then;
For perfect style in writin',
    at skweel, wi' ink and pen:
Licht wi' pen gan' up the page
    and heavy downward stroke,
Noo when I call tae mind a' this,
    it did me sair provoke.

I had tae learn the grammar
    so I could write wi' sense;
Nouns and punctuations,
    the adverbs and the tense:
I had tae learn the use o' words
    as so, and sew, and sow;
And get pronouncation right,
    like café, and depot.

I ha'e a braw typewriter noo,
  but hearken as I tell;
It oft forgets tae space the words,
  and och! it canna spell:
I tap on't wi' twa fing'rs,
  gratefa' aye tae hear
The little that I ha'e achieved,
gi'es pleasure far and near.

*now Kingswells School, Banff.

POWER CUT PONDERINGS

We hae nae mair a reekin' lum,
I licht the fire wi' flick o' thumb;
Nae ily lamp, as used tae be
We've a' geen tae 'lectricity.

Nae 'piggie' noo tae warm the bed,
A 'lectric blanket noo instead;
And if I hae tae rise wi' cramp
I aye switch on the bed-side lamp.

And if ye can affoord the cost
Ye get a 'thingie' tae mak' toast;
We mak' oor food on fancy cooker
Tae swipe the fleer we hae a sooker:
For labour-savin' washing days,
A braw machine tae wash the claes.

The present hoosewife has sic style,
But noo we're grudgin' coal and ile;
And when the mannie cuts the poo'er
This is indeed 'oor darkest oor';
Nae heat, nae licht, what will we dee?
Calamity! there's nae T.V.!
Modern life, the great 'rat race',
Grinds tae a halt, or slows the pace:
Sic problems then does Progress bring
Though maist would yet its praises sing;
But a'thing stops, that's plain tae see,
Withoot this great 'lectricity.

A FAIRMER'S FOLLY   *(Luke 12:16-21)*

I'll tell ye o' a fairmer chiel,
Lang, lang ago that promised weel;
And when at hairst his barns were fu',
He said, "I hae a problem noo,
I ken nae whaur I'll pit it a'
For och! this steadin's far ower sma'":
So he set tae wi' micht and main
Tae build a place tae haud his grain;
Aye thinkin' o' lang years o' pleasure,
He would hae wi' a' this treasure:
But as he wrocht wi' spadd and truel
There was a voice fae heaven, "Thou fool!
This nicht thy soul shall be required,
Then wha'll get a' ye hae acquired?"
So was he ta'en fae things he'd stored,
Tae meet the God he had ignored;
The hert is aye whaur treasure lies,
And thus he missed a heavenly prize.

So freen tak' heed, and noo be wise,
And nae the claims o' God despise;
He put us here tae show His glory,
And we hae failed - a gey sad story:
But there's anither side tae this,
We a' may win eternal bliss,
If we the Word o' God believe,
And Christ as Saviour we receive.

THE HALLELUJAH LINE *Jeremiah 33:3*

There's a telephone tae Glory
    if you wish tae mak' a call;
A Freephone Hallelujah Line
    available tae all:
Ye maun use the code-name 'Jesus'
    afore ye can get through,
And ony time, by nicht or day,
    oor God will answer you.

If ye want tae ken the number
    you will find it in the 'Book';
Turn tae Jeremiah,
    that's whaur ye hae tae look:
A promise is recorded there
    sae plain for a' tae see,
And that vital heavenly number
    chapter 33 and 3.

HOLY GROUND *Matthew 10:29*

I stood one day on holy ground,
A place where God must sure be found;
No great cathedral marked the place
And traffic sped with maddening pace:
No reverent step, nor breathless hush
Was known in all that haste and rush;
Men passed unheeding on their way,
None asked me why I paused that day
On sacred ground, of which I tell,
It was just where a sparrow fell.

The final flutter of those wings,
Formed by the Hand that made all things
A little life that there expired
Unseen by men, and undesired;
Was seen by Him who gave the sea
Its bounds - fixed by His firm decree;
And He who gave each star its place
In realms of vast, unmeasured space,
The eternal God, the Lord of all,
He saw that little sparrow fall.

TO MR. ALEX CLARK

Nae man can tether time nor tide,
   the years pass swiftly by;
We canna stop the march o' time
   however we may try:
And as you've reached retiring age
   by Government decree,
We hope - dear Alex, you will find,
   the best is yet tae be.

You've served Portessie bairns gey weel,
   for nine and twenty years;
You've listened tae their stories
   and seen the first-day tears;
Twa generations in your time,
   hae passed oot through the school;
Maist think o' you wi' high esteem
   for fair and kindly rule.

Nae mair tae work tae schedule time,
   wi' oors like eight tae five;
A 'lie-in' in the mornin'
   ye can aye contrive;
You'll note the time on pension day,
   wi' bookie in your hand,
You'll join the Senior Citizens
   that weel-respected band.

And noo since we are gaithered here,
   tae say a fond adieu;
Staff and pupils' grateful thanks
   are here passed on tae you:
We wish ye baith lang happy days
   guid health in fullest measure,
That you will gain life's finest worth,
   the best o' heavenly treasure.

*Written for the occasion of the retirement of Alex Clark, janitor at Portessie School.
The date was February 17th, 1987 and the poem was read at a farewell party with
staff and pupils and friends.*

65

TO JIMMY AND KINA. 1940 - 1990

Awa' back in a lang past day,
  when he was young and spry;
There was a lass fae Gardenstoon
  caught Jimmy Raffan's eye:
And when they made their mairriage vows,
  for better or for worse,
That day he got a bonnie bride
  a hoosemaid; cook; and nurse.

The year was nineteen forty
  the date the tenth o' May;
When Kina coyly promised
  tae honour and obey:
And as wi' freens ye celebrate
  this Golden Jubilee,
Oor prayer is that some happy years
  your portion yet will be.

We ken you've shared life's joys and tears,
  and trials hard tae bear;
And oft you've been wi' burdened hert,
  afore the Lord in prayer:
Whate'er the future yet may haud
  is in the Father's Hand,
So journey on, and praise His Name,
  for a' is wisely planned.

Golden Wedding celebration at Kildrummy Castle on 19th May, 1990.